This book belongs to

owen and Eric

Picnic Fun and Other Stories

How this collection works

This *Biff, Chip and Kipper* collection is one of a series of four books at **Read with Oxford Stage 1**. It is divided into two distinct halves.

The first half is designed to motivate your child to predict what might happen next, with two sets of 'Talk-about Situations': *Kipper's Talk-about Situations* and *Biff's Talk-about Situations*. The second half contains three stories that use everyday language: *Can You See Me?*, *The Headache* and *Picnic Fun*. These stories help to broaden your child's wider reading experience. There are also fun activities to enjoy throughout the book.

How to use this book

Find a time to read with your child when they are not too tired and are happy to concentrate for about ten minutes. Reading at this stage should be a shared and enjoyable experience. It is best to choose just one story or 'Talk-about Situation' for each session.

There are tips for each part of the book to help you make the most of the activities and stories. The tips for reading on pages 6 and 28 show you how to introduce your child to the predictive activities.

The tips for reading on pages 50, 62 and 74 explain how you can best approach reading the stories that use a wider vocabulary. At the end of each story you will find four 'Talk about the story' questions. These will help your child to think about what they have read, and to relate the story to their own experiences. The questions are followed by a fun activity.

Enjoy sharing the stories!

Authors and illustrators

Kipper's Talk-about Situations written by Roderick Hunt & Annemarie Young, illustrated by Alex Brychta

Biff's Talk-about Situations written by Roderick Hunt & Annemarie Young, illustrated by Alex Brychta

Can you see me? written by Roderick Hunt, illustrated by Alex Brychta

The Headache written by Roderick Hunt, illustrated by Alex Brychta

Picnic Fun written by Cynthia Rider, illustrated by Alex Brychta

OXFORD
UNIVERSITY PRESS

Great Clarendon Street, Oxford, OX2 6DP, United Kingdom

Oxford University Press is a department of the University of Oxford. It furthers the University's objective of excellence in research, scholarship, and education by publishing worldwide. Oxford is a registered trade mark of Oxford University Press in the UK and in certain other countries

The Headache first published 1995
Can you see me? first published 2003
Picnic Fun first published 2006
Kipper's Talk-about Situations, *Biff's Talk-about Situations* first published 2016
This Edition first published in 2018

British Library Cataloguing in Publication Data
Data available

ISBN: 978-0-19-276418-8

10 9 8 7 6 5 4 3 2

Paper used in the production of this book is a natural, recyclable product made from wood grown in sustainable forests. The manufacturing process conforms to the environmental regulations of the country of origin.

Printed in China

Acknowledgements

Series Editors: Annemarie Young and Kate Ruttle

Contents

OXFORD
UNIVERSITY PRESS

Phonics

Tips for reading *Kipper's Talk-about Situations*

Children learn best when reading is relaxed and enjoyable.

- Tell your child they are going to look at a series of pictures where something is about to happen.
- Talk about what is in the picture. Ask your child what is happening and what they think is going to happen next.
- Ask them to read any sound effect words in the picture, for example, 'Rat-a-tat-tat!'
- When you turn the page to see what actually happens, the outcome may or may not be what you expect! Talk about it.
- Ask your child to read the sound effect words in the picture (for example, 'Bam!'), and to read the simple sentence under the picture. All of the words on the outcome pages are phonically decodable.

Have fun!

Find the ten bugs hidden in the pictures.

The talk-about situations practise these
letter sounds:

a	i	o	u	e	b
d	f	h	kl	m	p
r	t	ss	ff	ll	ck

For more activities, free eBooks and practical advice to help your child progress with reading visit **oxfordowl.co.uk**

Kipper's Talk-about Situations

Find out what happens next!

Let's have some fun.

Talk about each picture.

Guess what's going to happen next!

8

What is Kipper doing?
What will happen next?

Kipper fell in the mud!

What are Mum and Dad doing?
What will happen next?

Mum fell. Dad fell off!

What will happen next?

The cat did not run!

What is Kipper doing?
What is Floppy doing?
What will happen next?

Kipper let go of the lid.

What is in the oven?
What is Dad going to do?

Bad luck, Dad!

What is making that noise?

It can tap and peck!

Mum got a kiss!

What is Kipper doing?
What will happen next?

A rip in the rabbit!

Matching

Match the sound words to the pictures.

Tick-tock!

Uck!

Bam!

Hiss!

Tap! Tap! Tap!

A maze

Follow Mum and Dad through the maze in the pram race.

FINISH

Read these sentences again

Kipper fell in the mud!

Bad luck, Dad!

Mum fell. Dad fell off!

It can tap and peck!

The cat did not run!

Mum got a kiss!

Kipper let go of the lid.

A rip in the rabbit!

Tips for reading *Biff's Talk-about Situations*

Children learn best when reading is relaxed and enjoyable.

- Tell your child they are going to look at a series of pictures where something is about to happen.

- Talk about what is in the picture. Ask your child what is happening and what they think is going to happen next.

- Ask them to read any sound effect words in the picture, for example 'Fizz!'

- When you turn the page to see what actually happens, the outcome may or may not be what you expect! Talk about it.

- Ask your child to read the sound effect words in the picture (for example, 'Pop!'), and to read the simple sentence under the picture. All of the words on the outcome pages are phonically decodable.

- Do the maze on page 48.

Find the six robins hidden in the pictures.

The talk-about situations practise these letter sounds:

j   w   x   y   zz   ll   ff   ss   ch   ck   ng   qu

For more activities, free eBooks and practical advice to help your child progress with reading visit **oxfordowl.co.uk**

Biff's Talk-about Situations

What is Kipper doing?
What is Mum saying?
What will happen next?

Kipper got wet!

What is Kipper doing? Why?
What will happen next?

It fell in the jug!

What are Dad and Biff doing?
What will happen next?

Dad had a miss.

What has Wilma found?
What will she do next?

Wilma put the duckling back.

What is the clown doing?
What will happen next?

Puff! Hiss! Fizz! Pop! Bang!

Lick! Lick!
Yum, yum!

puff!

What are the children waiting for?

The man rang the bell.

What is Gran doing?
What will happen next?

Gran fell into the box!

Matching

Match the sound words to the pictures.

Quack! Quack!

Ping! Pong!

Chuff chug!

Yuck!

Bang!

Ding dong!

A maze

Help the train get to the children.

Read these sentences and phrases again

Kipper got wet!

Puff! Hiss! Fizz! Pop! Bang!

It fell in the jug!

Lick! Lick! Yum, yum!

Dad had a miss.

The man rang the bell.

Wilma put the duckling back.

Gran fell into the box!

Stories for Wider Reading

Tips for reading the stories together

These three stories use simple everyday language. Encourage your child to read as much as they can with you. You can help your child to read any longer words, like 'time' and 'bridge', in the context of the story. Children enjoy re-reading stories and this helps to build their confidence and their vocabulary.

Tips for reading *Can You See Me?*

- Talk about the title and look through the pictures so that your child can see what the story is about.
- Read the story to your child, placing your finger under each word as you read.
- Read the story again and encourage your child to join in.
- Give lots of praise as your child reads with you.
- Talk about the story.
- Do the fun activity on page 60.

Have fun!

After you have read *Can you see me*, find the green frog in every picture.

This book includes these useful common words:

you   my   me

Can You See Me?

Can you see my ted?

Can you see my dog?

Can you see my big,
red frog?

Can you see my tiger?

Is it in the tree?

Can you see me?

Talk about the story

Where did you see Biff hiding?

How many toys can you see in Kipper's bedroom?

What other animals has Kipper painted?

What are your favourite toys?

Odd one out

Which is the odd one out? Say why.

Tips for reading *The Headache*

- Talk about the title and look through the pictures so that your child can see what the story is about.

- Read the story to your child, placing your finger under each word as you read.

- Read the story again and encourage your child to join in.

- Give lots of praise as your child reads with you.

- Talk about the story.

- Do the fun activity on page 72.

Have fun!

The Headache

Dad had a trumpet.

Chip had a drum.

Biff had a recorder.

Kipper had a guitar.

Mum had a headache!

Talk about the story

What are the four instruments in the story?

Which one did Kipper have?

Why did Mum have a headache?

What instrument would you like to play? Why?

Odd one out

What are these instruments? Which one is not
in the story?

Tips for reading *Picnic Fun*

- Talk about the title and look through the pictures so that your child can see what the story is about.

- Read the story to your child, placing your finger under each word as you read.

- Read the story again and encourage your child to join in.

- Give lots of praise as your child reads with you.

- Talk about the story.

- Do the fun activity on page 94.

Have fun!

After you have read *Can You See Me?* find the green frog hidden in every picture.

This story includes these useful common words:

said   on   some   came

 For more activities, free eBooks and practical advice to help your child progress with reading visit **oxfordowl.co.uk**

Picnic Fun

Find out why the children ran away!

"Picnic time!" said Dad.

Biff sat on a log.

Some sheep came.

"Run!" said Kipper.

They sat on a bridge.

Some ducks came.

"Run!" said Chip.

They sat on a wall.

Some donkeys came.

"Run!" said Biff.

They sat on a rock.

Oh no! The rain came!

Talk about the story

What happened when Biff gave the duck some bread?

Why did the children run away from the animals?

Where was the picnic? How do you know?

What food would you like to take on a picnic?

Tangled lines

Who will get the picnic?

Remembering the stories together

Encourage your child to remember and retell the three stories in this book. You could ask questions like these:

- Who are the characters in the story?
- What happens at the beginning of the story?
- What happens next?
- How does the story end?
- What was your favourite part of the story? Why?

Story prompts

When talking to your child about the stories, you could use these more detailed reminders to help them remember the exact sequence of events. Turn the statements below into questions, so that your child can give you the answers. For example, *Who is Kipper looking for first? Then who's he looking for?* And so on …

Can You See Me?

- Kipper is looking for his ted.
- Now he's looking for his dog, Floppy.
- He's looking for his picture of a red frog.
- He's looking for his toy tiger.
- Can you find Kipper?

The Headache

- Dad is playing the trumpet.

- Chip is playing the drum.

- Biff is playing the recorder.

- Kipper is playing the guitar.

- And Mum has a headache!

Picnic Fun

- The family are having a picnic.

- The children are sitting on a log when some sheep come along.

- The sheep want the children's picnic, so they chase the children.

- The children are sitting on a bridge when some ducks come along.

- They are sitting on a wall and some donkeys want their picnic.

- Then the rain gets them wet!

You could now encourage your child to create a 'story map' of each story, drawing and colouring all the key parts of them. This will help them to identify the main elements of the stories and learn to create their own stories.